PURRFECT GREETINGS

18 cat cards to color in and send

Publishers: Isabelle Jeuge-Maynart and Ghislaine Stora
Editorial Director: Sylvie Cattaneo-Naves
Editor: Barbara Janssens
Cover: Claire Morel-Fatio
Layout: Sophie Compagne, Jack Storey
Production Controller: Allison Gonsalves

An Hachette UK company
www.hachette.co.uk

First published in France in 2016 by Dessain et Tolra

This edition published in Great Britain in 2016 by Hamlyn,
a division of Octopus Publishing Group Ltd,
Carmelite House, 50 Victoria Embankment, London EC4Y 0DZ
www.octopusbooksusa.com

Copyright © Dessain et Tolra/Larousse 2016
English translation © Octopus Publishing Group Ltd 2016

Distributed in the US by Hachette Book Group
1290 Avenue of the Americas, 4th and 5th Floors
New York, NY 10020

Distributed in Canada by Canadian Manda Group
664 Annette St., Toronto, Ontario, Canada M6S 2C8

ISBN 978 0 600 63429 4

Printed and bound in China
10 9 8 7 6 5 4 3 2 1

Color

Write

Fold

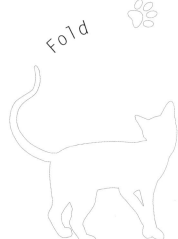

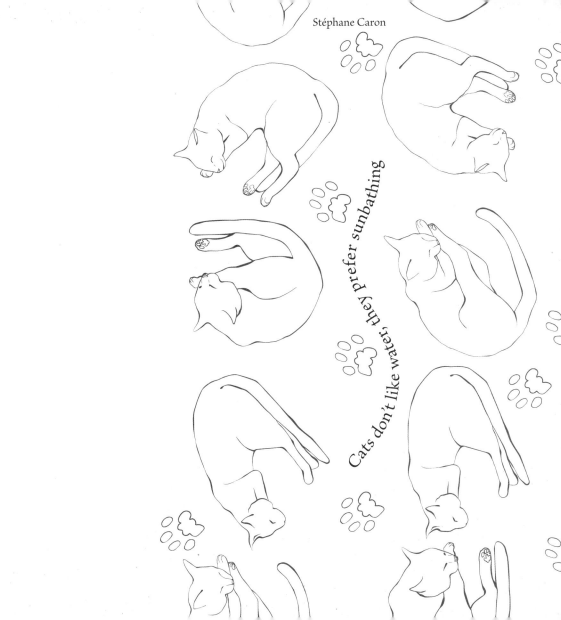

Stéphane Caron

Cats don't like water, they prefer sunbathing

Cats don't like water, they prefer sunbathing
Stéphane Caron

Cats are made to store caresses.
Stéphane Mallarmé

Cats are made to store caresses.
Stéphane Mallarmé

When I am playing with my cat, how do I know she is not playing with me?
Michel de Montaigne

When I am playing
with my cat, how
do I know she is not
playing with me?

Michel
de Montaigne

The quintessence of calm is a seated cat.
Jules Renard

The quintessence of calm is a seated cat.
Jules Renard

Cats are smart and know it.
Tomi Ungerer

Cats are smart and know it.

Tomi Ungerer

When a cat gives her confidence to a man,

this is his best gift.

Charles Darwin

When a cat gives her confidence to a man, this is his best gift.
Charles Darwin

Time spent with cats is never wasted.
Colette

Time spent with cats is never wasted.
Colette

Purring is the
smile of a cat.
Hector Biancotti

Purring is the smile of a cat.
Hector Biancotti

You never choose a cat. He chooses you.
Philippe Ragueneau

You never choose a cat. He chooses you.
Philippe Ragueneau

The cat is beautiful; it arouses ideas of luxury, cleanliness, and voluptuousness.

Charles Baudelaire

The cat is beautiful; it arouses ideas of luxury, cleanliness, and voluptuousness.
Charles Baudelaire

A cat is not bound to live by the laws of a lion.
Baruch Spinoza

A cat is not bound to live by the laws of a lion.

Baruch Spinoza

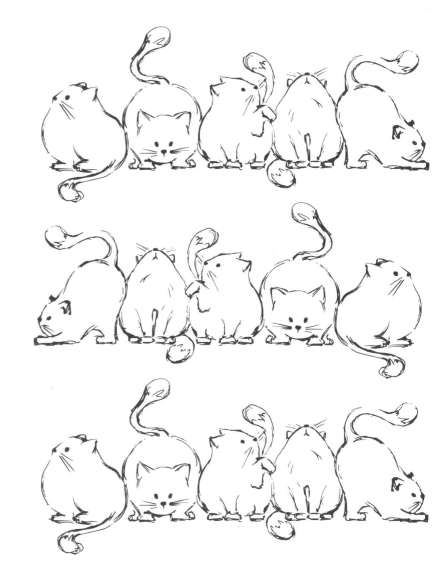

What greater gift than the love of a cat?
Charles Dickens

What greater gift than the love of a cat?

Charles Dickens

The smallest feline is a masterpiece.
Leonardo da Vinci

The smallest feline is a masterpiece.

Leonardo da Vinci

A cat pours his body on the floor like water.
William Lyon Phelps

A cat pours his body on the floor like water.
William Lyon Phelps

The key

to a successful

new relationship

between a cat and human

is patience.

Susan Easterly

The key to a successful new relationship between a cat and human is patience.
Susan Easterly

I love cats because I enjoy my home; and little by little, they become its visible soul.
Jean Cocteau

I love cats
because I
enjoy my home;
and little by
little, they
become its
visible soul.

Jean Cocteau

If you are
worthy of its
affection, a cat
will be your
friend but never
your slave.
Théophile Gautier

If you are worthy of its affection, a cat will be your friend
but never your slave.
Théophile Gautier

There are two means of refuge from the miseries of life:
music and cats.
Albert Schweitzer

There are two means of refuge from the
miseries of life: music and cats.
Albert Schweitzer